TRIGGER WARNING

This journal engages with deep and often challenging aspects of personal development, such as emotional trauma, attachment styles, personal insecurities, and the navigation of psychological complexities. It is designed to facilitate self-reflection and growth.

Please approach the exercises with care. If any content brings up distressing emotions or overwhelming thoughts, prioritize your emotional safety and consider seeking the support of a qualified mental health professional. This journal is not a substitute for professional psychological services or medical advice.

The publisher and author of this journal assume no liability for any direct or indirect losses or damages that may result due to the use of this journal. By proceeding with the use of this journal, you agree to do so at your own risk, and understand that it is a self-help tool intended for those who are ready and willing to embark on a journey of self-exploration.

Remember to move at a pace that feels right for you and to practice self-compassion throughout your journey.

WORKBOOK

INTRODUCTION

HOW TO HEAL AN AVOIDANT ATTACHMENT STYLE

"The first step towards getting somewhere is to decide you're not going to stay where you are."

Why **hey there avoidant**, fancy seeing you here. Usually **you would avoid this type of thing** (obviously), so just being here is a **massive first step.**

How to Heal an Avoidant Attachment Style is here to guide you through your next ones.

Together, we'll delve into the **origins of your avoidant attachment style**, examine **how your subconscious programming** has been impacting your **relationships**, learn techniques to **rewire the mind**, dive into **shadow work** journalling to **heal past trauma** and finally focus on **envisioning your desired future.**

You've probably never tried a journal quite like this before**, so here's a little preview of what to expect.**

Think of it like a **trusty friend** (we know trusting is **hard for you** - we'll work on it) who's **great at listening** and has some **cool insights** that you've never thought of before.

Why shadow work, you might ask? The answer is **simple**.

It's a powerful psychological model that helps you **discover hidden aspects of your personality**, your 'shadow,' that often **dictates your actions and reactions** in ways you might not even be fully aware of.

We'll guide you through **comprehending the role of your 'shadow'** and utilizing this understanding for **healing**.

We've curated a set of prompts aimed at promoting s**elf-reflection, understanding, and personal growth.**

Most importantly, we we'll equip you with practical tools and techniques to **heal your avoidant attachment style.**

Before we dive in, **take a moment** to think about what you want to achieve on your journey.

We know you struggle with vulnerability, but **are you ready to truly open up and be real with yourself?**

Yeah? **Cool, let's do this.**

CHAPTER 1

UNDERSTANDING AVOIDANT ATTACHMENT STYLE

“Avoidance is a simple way of coping by not having to cope”

- Lori Gottllieb

UNDERSTANDING AVOIDANT ATTACHMENT STYLE

Attachment Theory

First things first, let's learn a bit about **attachment theory.**

Attachment theory, at its core, is all about our **connections with others.**

It's a psychological model that attempts to describe the **dynamics of long-term relationships between humans.**

But it's not just any relationship, it's the **deep, emotional bond that forms between a child and their caregivers**, and how these early experiences of love and connection **influence us in our adult relationships.**

Biologically speaking, **humans are wired for connection**.

It's not just a **feel-good, optional part of life.**

It's essential for survival.

In our earliest years, **forming an emotional bond with caregivers is vital** because it directly influences a **child's safety and well-being**.

The child's attachment to a caregiver is a **survival mechanism that promotes basic needs,** triggering the **caregiver's instinctual response to provide care.**

The **impact of these bonds extend far beyond childhood.**

These formative experiences don't just fade away; **they embed themselves in your subconscious mind,** becoming a kind of **automatic programming** that dictates **how you approach relationships** and emotional situations **as an adult.**

Types of Attachment Styles

There are **4 main types of attachment styles**, each with its unique characteristics, strengths, and areas for growth. Here are the basics:

Anxious Attachment Style

People with an **anxious attachment style** often experience a deep-seated fear of abandonment, coupled with insecurity and a desire to feel needed.

This attachment style tends to emerge from experiences in early childhood where emotional needs were inconsistently met, leading to **heightened anxiety in relationships**. They may also have a **fear of rejection.**

They tend to have a higher need for closeness and may experience **more frequent and intense emotions in their relationships.**

Disorganized Attachment Style

Also known as **fearful-avoidant,** this style is characterized by a combination of anxious and avoidant tendencies.

People with a fearful-avoidant attachment style may have a **fear of both rejection and intimacy**. They may desire close relationships but also feel anxious about getting hurt or rejected.

They may exhibit contradictory behaviors, such as **pushing others away while simultaneously longing for connection**.

Secure Attachment Style

People with a secure attachment style feel **comfortable with both intimacy and independence.**

They trust their caregivers and **feel secure in their relationships.** As adults, they tend to have **healthy** and **balanced** relationships, with good communication, trust, and emotional support.

This is what we're aiming for!

Understanding Avoidant Attachment Style

Now, let's get to the important one, **the reason you're here.**

An avoidant attachment style is characterized by a significant **emphasis on independence and emotional self-reliance.**

This isn't just a preference for solo time or space in a relationship; it's a **deeply ingrained wariness of becoming too emotionally entangled with someone else.**

When you start to feel cornered by emotional demands or intimacy, **your internal alarm system kicks in**.

It activates protective measures like the **freeze response** that induces; **hypervigilance, emotional detachment and total withdrawal.**

Your defence mechanisms activate and **you emotionally shut everything down.**

Don't be too hard on yourself if you recognize this in your own behavior; as we've already explored **your attachment style is most likely a product of your early life experiences.**

You may have been raised in a home **where emotional expression was discouraged** or **where independence was overly emphasized.**

Your caregivers might have been **inconsistent in their affection** or **emotionally unavailable altogether.**

Maybe they were just busy trying to support the family or **dealing with their own struggles and unintentionally neglected your needs.**

These experiences often lead to a focus on **self-preservation**, even at the **expense of meaningful emotional connections.**

People with an avoidant attachment style **may scrutinize their partners for flaws** or **keep an emotional scorecard**, not as a way to keep the relationship in check, but **as a way to justify their emotional distance.**

By doing this, you're not necessarily pushing others away intentionally, but **you're safeguarding yourself from the vulnerabilities** that come with emotional intimacy.

Causes of an Avoidant Attachment Style

Now let's try to identify **how you developed your avoidant attachment style.**

Highlight or **circle** the causes below that **resonate with you:**

Emotional Unavailability of Parent/s

Childhood Roots: When the people responsible for your well-being were indifferent or unresponsive to your emotional needs, you naturally learned to downplay the importance of those needs. You adapted by internalizing your emotions, learning that emotional availability from others is unreliable at best.

Adult Reinforcement: This manifests as a hesitance to fully emotionally invest in your partners. You've become adept at offering the bare minimum of emotional involvement, enough to maintain the relationship but not so much that you feel at risk of emotional pain or disappointment.

Defensive Independence

Childhood Roots: In a household where stringent expectations were the norm, displaying vulnerability often invited criticism rather than compassion. Your emotional self-expression was stunted as you adapted to your parents' high expectations, internalizing the message that it's better to manage your feelings independently to avoid judgment.

Adult Reinforcement: You've become used to handling your emotional struggles alone. The hesitance to expose vulnerabilities makes it a challenge to engage in the kind of open, emotionally supportive relationships that many find fulfilling.

Parental Mental Health

Childhood Roots: Growing up with a parent struggling with depression or other mental health issues could mean experiencing emotional neglect or inconsistency. On good days, your parent might have shown affection or engaged with you, but on their low days, they likely withdrew, becoming emotionally unavailable.

Adult Reinforcement: This inconsistency might have programmed you to handle emotional issues solo, never quite sure if seeking support would be met with warmth or indifference. You might be reluctant to share emotional burdens with your partner, as you've learned to equate seeking help with potential disappointment or neglect.

High Standards & Perfectionism

Childhood Roots: Raised in an environment where the bar was set exceptionally high, you were implicitly—or explicitly—taught that love and approval were contingent upon your achievements and behavior. This created an incessant pressure to be perfect, making you keenly aware of your own flaws and failures. Any shortfall was not just a simple mistake but a mark against your worthiness for emotional support and affection.

Adult Reinforcement: You find yourself not only demanding perfection from yourself but your partners too. You have a tendency to judge your partners and create standards so high that they can't be met. Over time, your high standards turn into high walls, limiting the depth and richness of emotional connections you could otherwise enjoy.

Traumatic Events

Childhood Roots: Experiencing traumatic events in childhood significantly alters your perception of safety and emotional well-being. These events could range from accidents, the loss of a loved one, to extreme forms of emotional or physical abuse. The trauma teaches you, at a young age, that vulnerability can be hazardous, making it imperative to construct an emotional armor for self-preservation.

Adult Reinforcement: You've learned to associate emotional openness with potential danger or pain, leading you to control the emotional temperature of your interactions meticulously. This emotional distance you maintain serves as both a shield and a barrier, protecting you from perceived threats but also preventing meaningful, intimate connections.

Busy Parent/s

Childhood Roots: If you grew up with parents who were constantly busy—be it with work, social commitments, or other pursuits—you likely experienced periods of emotional unavailability from them. Even if they provided for you materially, their hectic schedules could have resulted in neglecting emotional check-ins or meaningful interactions.

Adult Reinforcement: This environment might have taught you to fend for yourself emotionally, equating independence with emotional safety. In your adult relationships, this manifests as a tendency to tackle challenges alone, hesitant to lean on a partner for fear of being an inconvenience or burden.

Sibling Dynamics

Childhood Roots: Growing up amidst intense sibling rivalry or competition can be more than just a family dynamic; it can shape your very understanding of attachment and emotional intimacy. The competition for parental attention or resources might have taught you that emotional connections are transactional or unstable.

Adult Reinforcement: These early experiences can manifest as a hesitancy to truly invest emotionally. The competitive dynamics you learned in your family might make you view emotional intimacy as a zero-sum game where vulnerability could mean losing out. These habits persistently influence your interactions, making it challenging to form deep, stable bonds.

Parental Alienation

Childhood Roots: Parental alienation usually occurs when one parent speaks negatively about the other, this can be during divorce, separation or even when still living under the same roof. It might even be that your parent confided in you and spent time venting their frustrations about your other parent.This form of emotional manipulation can instill a deep mistrust of emotional closeness.

Adult Reinforcement: This foundation of mistrust can surface as a fear of manipulation or emotional exploitation. It can make you extremely cautious in letting anyone get too close, reinforcing your avoidant tendencies.

Emotional Suppression

Childhood Roots: In households where emotional expression was frowned upon or even punished, you learn to tightly control your feelings and desires. You grow up believing that emotions are liabilities, better kept at arm's length. This environment is ripe for the development of an avoidant attachment style, where emotional suppression becomes a coping mechanism.

Adult Reinforcement: Opening up emotionally may feel like you're crossing a line you were taught never to approach. This can make it incredibly difficult to form an emotional connection, as you instinctively retreat into your protective shell whenever vulnerability is on the horizon.

Social & Cultural Reinforcement

Childhood Roots: Social experiences outside the home also played a role. Whether it was peer rejection, bullying, or simply cultural norms that glorify emotional stoicism, these social factors reinforced your inclination to keep emotional distance. The collective message was clear: showing vulnerability is a weakness, and emotional self-reliance is the gold standard.

Adult Reinforcement: You might find yourself modeling or gravitating towards relationships that align with these socially reinforced beliefs. Being 'cool' and 'unattached' often gets validation, whether it's through media or social circles, fortifying your existing avoidant tendencies. The perpetual reinforcement from society at large makes it difficult to break free from this pattern.

Unresolved Past Relationships

Adult Origin: While many attachment behaviors take root in childhood, some are born out of adult experiences. Relationships that ended poorly, were emotionally draining, or caused significant emotional upheaval can impact your attachment tendencies in meaningful ways. These failed or painful relationships introduce a new layer of emotional baggage, influencing how you approach intimacy and emotional investment in future partnerships.

Adult Reinforcement: As you forge new relationships, the shadows of these unresolved past relationships frequently resurface, especially when facing emotional closeness or conflict. These past experiences reinforce your hesitance to fully emotionally invest in a new partner. The natural inclination is to retreat into avoidant behaviors, which serve as a form of emotional self-preservation. This pattern keeps you at a safe distance, making it increasingly difficult to form intimate, fulfilling relationships.

Circle the traits below that resonate with you.

If your parent was:		You:
Critical	⟷	Are a harsh self critic and a perfectionist.
Passive Aggressive	⟷	Struggle to communicate & have difficulty expressing yourself
Unapproving	⟷	Seek external validation.
Too Busy	⟷	Have a fear of abandonment
Co-dependent	⟷	Struggle to set boundaries
Dismissive	⟷	Underestimate your self worth
Judgmental	⟷	Fear being judged
Overprotective	⟷	Are indecisive and fear independence.
Emotionally Distant	⟷	Struggle with closeness
Manipulative	⟷	Have deep trust issues
Shaming	⟷	Carry internal shame
Overly Involved	⟷	Are confused about who you are
Stoic	⟷	Struggle with communication
Perfectionist	⟷	Fear failure
Overachiever	⟷	Feel pressure to perform and excel.
Competitive	⟷	Are unhealthily competitive

Signs of an Avoidant Attachment Style

Now that you have some idea of how you **developed your attachment style,** let's look at what an **avoidant attachment style looks like in everyday life.**

Highlight or **circle** the **signs** below that **resonate with you:**

- **Avoidance of Emotional Intimacy:** You often shy away from deep emotional discussions or affection, considering them unnecessary and uncomfortable.
- **Suppressing Feelings:** Even if you're experiencing strong feelings for someone, you're likely to bottle them up rather than sharing openly.
- **Valuing Independence Over Connection:** You prioritize independence to the point where it hinders you from forming deep relationships.
- **Difficulty Accepting Support:** You're likely to decline or deflect emotional support, preferring to handle things on your own even when it's not in your best interest. You often view relying on others as a sign of weakness.
- **Detachment During Conflict:** Instead of confronting issues and working through them, you're more likely to retreat and create emotional distance.
- **Dismissive of Needs:** You might not be attuned to your partner's emotional needs or might dismiss them as being too needy or clingy, not recognizing this as a normal aspect of a balanced relationship.
- **Unwilling to Reveal Vulnerabilities:** You keep your weaknesses and fears closely guarded, considering emotional vulnerability as giving others power over you.
- **Skeptical of True Love:** A dose of skepticism often colors your view of love, questioning the feasibility of long-term happiness in romantic relationships.
- **Self-Sabotage Tactics:** You engage in behavior that derails potential connections, like imposing unattainable standards or focusing on minor flaws to justify leaving.
- **Reluctance to Commit:** You find yourself hesitating or dodging commitment, often fearing it might compromise your freedom.

Triggers for an Avoidant Attachment

Spotting your **triggers** helps you **understand why you may emotionally distance yourself** or resort to **self-reliance** at the expense of deeper connections.

Highlight or **circle** the **triggers** below that **resonate with you:**

- **Emotional Demands:** When someone asks for emotional support or a deeper level of commitment, you might pull away, feeling burdened or trapped.
- **Clingy or 'Needy' Behavior:** You feel suffocated when someone is being too needy, triggering you to withdraw emotionally.
- **Vulnerability:** Sharing weaknesses or discussing emotional hardships can make you uncomfortable, pushing you to change the subject or distance yourself.
- **Jealousy or Possessiveness:** You see jealousy and possessiveness as a sign that your partner is trying to control you.
- **Breaks in Routine:** A sudden change in your own routine creates anxiety around a loss of control.
- **Expressed Insecurities:** Hearing your partner express doubt or insecurities can compel you to consider whether the emotional investment is worth it.
- **Challenges to Independence:** Any event or behavior that seems to interrupt or infringe on your personal freedom or self-reliance.
- **Intense Emotional Moments:** Situations that require emotional openness and exchange, particularly if it's about negative or sensitive topics.
- **Conflict or Confrontation:** Disagreements or criticisms can make you emotionally shut down, avoiding the issue rather than facing it head-on.
- **High-Stakes Situations:** Major life events, such as meeting the family can ramp up your resistance and avoidance mechanisms, even if things in the relationship have been going smoothly.
- **Talks About the Future:** Any discussions about long-term plans, moving in together, or any other form of commitment may provoke an internal resistance.

By identifying these **signs** and **triggers**, you can work towards **preemptive strategies and coping mechanisms.**

Rating Your Avoidant Attachment Style

This exercise uses a straightforward rating system to help you **evaluate your avoidant attachment tendencies.**

Rate **how true each one feels for you** on a scale of **1 (rarely true) to 10 (always true):**

- ☐ I often find faults in people who want to get close to me.
- ☐ Emotional conversations generally make me uncomfortable.
- ☐ I don't like it when people rely on me emotionally.
- ☐ I am described as emotionally unavailable, cold or distant.
- ☐ I purposely suppress my own emotions.
- ☐ I often keep my problems to myself.
- ☐ When someone expresses their feelings for me, I pull away.
- ☐ Being vulnerable feels like weakness.
- ☐ Emotional intimacy feels like a threat to my personal freedom.
- ☐ I avoid discussing the future of my relationships.

- **Low Score (1-20):** Your avoidant attachment tendencies are mild. Even a minimal awareness of what triggers these tendencies can be extremely beneficial for your personal growth.
- **Medium Score (21-50):** You exhibit moderate levels of avoidant attachment behavior. There's some work to do to address the answers that you scored high on.
- **High Score (51+):** Your tendencies toward avoidant attachment are quite strong and may require more focused effort to address.

Reflection & Improvement

So, you've looked into the **causes, signs and triggers** of your **avoidant attachment style**, now it's time to focus on those areas where you see **room for growth.**

Turn your attention to the statements where you rated yourself between **6 and 10** in the previous **avoidant attachment exercise.**

For each of these elevated scores, **consider setting a specific objective** or gaining an insight you'd like to achieve.

Example:

- If you scored high on: "**I avoid discussing the future of my relationships.**"
- Your goal could be: "I want to become **more comfortable discussing my emotions and communicating** about the future with my partner".

This exercise will serve as a **reference point** you can revisit as you journey through this journal.

It's a way to make sure you're **aligning the work** you're doing with the **goals and changes you aspire to see in yourself.**

What would you like to improve on?

CHAPTER 2

THE POWER OF YOUR SUBCONSCIOUS MIND

"The subconscious mind is the guiding force of all our life experiences."

- Joseph Murphy

THE POWER OF YOUR SUBCONSCIOUS MIND

Getting Stuck in Thought Loops

Did you know, your subconscious mind is **on a constant loop?**

You've thought around **90% of the same thoughts** today as you did yesterday - this is your very own version of **"auto-pilot".**

It's always there, always active, **shaping the story you live every day**.

Think of it like a program that's **always running in the background without you realizing it.**

From your subconscious mind spring all of your **thoughts, feelings, habits**, and ultimately, **your lived reality.**

It's really hard to **break this cycle of thought**, especially when **you're not aware of it.**

So, what are you thinking about?

The subconscious mind stores all of your **memories, beliefs, values, past experiences and trauma.**

If you're someone who has unresolved issues, past trauma, resentment, fear or anxiety, the likelihood is that your **subconscious narrative** or **"the voice in your head" is mostly fearful, negative and full of anxiety**.

For example, if you've experienced trauma that has lead to the belief that "**I'll never find the right person for me**" your subconscious programming will **continue to reiterate** and **confirm that belief.**

Not only will your programming continue to reiterate to you that **"no one is right for you"**, it will **look for evidence** in your life to **prove that it's true.**

From the moment you're born, your subconscious mind begins to **store** and **learn from every experience, every emotion, every belief,** and **all the information you encounter and create your program.**

Understanding this is the key to everything.

Childhood Programming

We start to establish our **subconscious programming** between the ages of **0-7 years old.**

During this time, **both hemispheres of the brain are firing** and **absorbing** everything around us **like a sponge.**

This is where we start to become conditioned by our **families, friends, schools, religious beliefs and society**.

Through this conditioning, we begin to develop our own **personal identity** or **"self concept".**

By the time you reach 8 years old **the majority of your assumptions and belief systems are deeply ingrained in the subconscious mind** and will **continue to affect your behaviour into adulthood.**

So, in essence, all of your ingrained beliefs, assumptions and influences from childhood are **still triggering your subconscious mind today.**

You just don't realize it.

Your childhood programming is your baseline - **your mind and body's comfort zone.**

The mind will fight to **stay in the 'known'** - even if that means living the **same stories of pain and trauma over and over again for a lifetime.**

Resisting this programming means **confronting your negative thoughts** and literally **telling yourself what to think.**

We are going to **intentionally disrupt** your subconscious programming and introduce **new information** to free you from **limiting and anxious beliefs.**

By **intentionally changing your thought patterns** you will create **new neural connections in the brain.**

This is called **neuroplasticity,** which will help you to **rewire your mind** and create **a new subconscious program.**

Let's begin by **focusing on your self concept.**

Changing Your Self Concept

The question now is, **who are you**? What do you **believe about yourself**?

Let's dive into the importance of understanding your **self concept**. **Why?**

Because **how you perceive yourself** is the core of **everything that you are** and **everything that you attract.**

Self concept is the story you tell yourself about **who you are.**

It shapes how you **interact with the world** and **how the world interacts with you.**

It **influences all of your choices.**

You might think that you're making decisions **based on your current thoughts and experiences**, but often, these choices are **heavily influenced by limiting** **deep-seated beliefs** and **narratives about yourself.**

For example if you grew up with the belief that "**you have to fight to receive love**", this could subconsciously lead to **choosing avoidant partners who** **reaffirm this belief.**

We need to figure out what **ingrained beliefs** are **holding you back** to start to **shift your self concept.**

And guess what? If you stick to it, it takes just **30 days to create a new neural pathway**.

Pretty cool that you can **rewire your brain**, right?

That, **if you just tried**, you could **become whoever** and **believe whatever you want.**

So, **what's the story you tell about yourself?**

Right now, your **subconscious mind is your inner-critic.**

Whatever you believe about yourself is true.

But you can **change your beliefs** and **we're going to teach you how.**

This isn't about putting on a mask or **pretending to be someone you're not.**

It's about **letting go of any subconscious blockages** or **negative internalized beliefs**, it's about becoming **the best version of you.**

Your Self Concept

On the next page draw lines radiating out from "**My Self Concept**", like a web.

- At the end of each line, write a belief or assumption you hold about yourself, others, or the world.
- **Be as honest as possible.**

Answer the following:

- **Who Are You?** How would you describe yourself in a few words?
- **Self-Image**: How do you feel about your appearance?
- **Life:** Do you believe life is fair or unfair? Why?
- **Love**: Do you believe in love? Do you believe you deserve real love?
- **Meaning of Life:** What does being alive mean to you?
- **Life's Purpose:** What do you think your life's purpose is?
- **Opinions**: How much do you think others' opinions about you matter?
- **Life Stage**: Are you satisfied with where you are in life right now?
- **Control:** Do you feel in control of your life and decisions?
- **Expectations**: Do you find yourself burdened by others' expectations?
- **Self Love:** Do you like yourself and treat yourself well?
- **Finances:** How do you feel about your current financial stability?
- **Change:** Do you believe you have the ability to change your life?
- **Future**: Are you optimistic or pessimistic about what the future holds?

- Once completed look at your Belief Web.
  - Are there any beliefs that **surprise you**? Any **patterns**? Any beliefs that might be **holding you back** from fully accepting yourself?

- **Circle or highlight the beliefs** you want to work on changing throughout your journey.

Your Dream Self

Close your eyes and envision the best version of yourself.

- Sit with this vision for a minute and **feel** it as if this is you right now.
- Pay attention to how you look, how you feel, what you do for work, who's around you, where you live.

Draw lines radiating out from **"My Dream Self"**, like a web.

- Answer the same questions above, from the **perspective of your dream self.**

My Self Concept

My Dream Self

Rewiring Your Nervous System

When your self concept is largely **negative** and you find yourself stuck in a mental loop, **replaying the same stories and scenarios over and over again**, there's more happening beneath the surface than just a "busy mind."

These repetitive thought patterns can actually have a **physiological impact on you.**

When you **suppress your emotions** and your thought patterns are **negative, avoidant, or anchored in past traumas** it can lead to a **disregulated nervous system.**

What does that mean?

Well, it **throws your stress response mechanisms out of whack**, making it **more challenging to cope with day-to-day pressures.**

These incessant loops **contribute to your body's production of stress hormones like cortisol and adrenaline**, setting off a domino effect that can influence everything from **your mood to your immune system**.

Your mind is **panicking** and so is your body.

As an avoidant attachment your body tends to to experience the **dorsal vagal state** or **"functional freeze".**

When in **"functional freeze"** you experience an emotional **"shutdown" response to extreme stress.**

This can look like **disassociation**, **disconnection**, not being able to **cry**, feeling **emotionally numb** or not feeling **present**.

This cycle of biochemical responses **keeps you stuck.**

The subconscious mind **clings to the stories you tell yourself,** the **emotions you suppress**, the **memories you sit with** and continues to **send the same thoughts to you over and over again.**

Breaking free from these repetitive thought loops isn't just about achieving mental clarity; it's about **recalibrating an entire system** — **your mind-body network.**

Awareness & Listening to Your Thoughts

Now that you have an awareness of your subconscious loop, **it's time to disrupt it.**

Your internal dialogue is geared towards **self preservation** and has a way of **creating emotional turbulence.**

You're **keenly aware** of any attempt to **breach your emotional boundaries**, always on the lookout for signs that **someone is getting too close for comfort.**

Your subconscious convinces you that **maintaining your autonomy** is the key to your well-being, reinforcing your cycle of emotional detachment.

Remember, the **body doesn't know the difference between a thought and a real experience.**

Every time you think **about that fight from a few weeks ago**, or a **bad childhood memory**, or that **ex that cheated on you,** your brain thinks it's happening **<u>right now</u>**.

Can you see how that's a problem?

Your **internal alarms are always activated** and we need to start working on that.

Here's the truth: **<u>it's you vs you here.</u>**

You're **challenging your default programming** by interrupting it and sending it new messaging.

You're taking control by understanding that **<u>you are not your thoughts</u> - crazy, right?**

The more you **pay attention to what's going on in your brain,** the more you can actively **choose your thoughts.**

When your brain starts to hear **positive thoughts** as opposed to **negative or fearful thoughts**, it **starts to believe them.**

It's like giving yourself a **software update,** that loop that you've been stuck in for **months, years or even decades; we're about to change it.**

Make sense?

Are you ready to start **rewiring the mind together?**

CHAPTER 3

TECHNIQUES TO REWIRE YOUR BRAIN

"If you want a new outcome, you will have to break the habit of being yourself, and reinvent a new self."

- Dr. Joe Dispenza

TECHNIQUES TO REWIRE YOUR BRAIN

Let's **take back control** of your mind, shall we?

Make a commitment out loud to yourself right now, say: **"I am going to start listening to my thoughts**" - this is setting a reminder for your brain.

Now let's **start practicing.**

1. Catching & Challenging

The first technique is **catching and challenging your thoughts.**

What's something that has been consistently popping up in your mind that is causing you to create avoidant or negative thoughts? Write about what it is and what you keep thinking about.

We're going to use this situation **as a test.**

For the next few weeks, every time you think about this situation, try to **catch the thought.**

It sounds **a little weird,** but now that you have an **awareness** of your **loop** you're going to see that your **brain runs off on tangents all the time** without you even consciously realizing it.

Once you catch the thought "**observe it**".

Challenge it.

- ***Why are you thinking it?***
- ***Is the thought valid?***
- ***Do you agree?***
- ***Is this thought rooted in avoidance?***
- ***Where did the thought come from?***
- ***Has this thought been on loop for more than one day?***
- ***What can you do about the thought?***

Interrupt the thought - literally - **tell yourself to stop.**

Don't allow yourself to **think negatively** and **feed your avoidant narrative.**

Shift your focus to something else and **continue to do this as often as possible when you catch the thought.**

2. Affirmations

Throughout your **shadow work journalling journey** we want you to practice **an affirmation.**

And here's why.

Using positive affirmations is **a powerful way to influence your subconscious mind.**

This is also an **amazing** way to **stop yourself from mentally spiralling;** when you feel like your **thoughts are out of control - repeat your affirmation.**

Keep repeating it until you've **interrupted the thought so much** that you've forgotten it and **can think about something else.**

Remember, **you think around 90% of the same subconscious thoughts everyday.**

When you repeat positive affirmations you're **feeding the brain new information** and **creating new neural pathways** that will help you to **shift your programming.**

You can practice your affirmations **either inside your head or out loud.**

To enhance your practice we recommend:

- **Attaching a Feeling to your Affirmation**
  - Don't just say the words, **feel the words** as deeply as you can;
  - **Visualize** how you'd feel **right now** if these words were true and **let that feeling envelop your body,**
  - Feeling the words as if they're true right now, acts as a kind of **trick** to the mind and body,
  - The body will respond to these positive feelings by **releasing seratonin** as it **believes the truth of the affirmation,**
  - **Feeling** is a major key for affirmations - **remember this!**

- **Practicing a Morning & Night Affirmation**
  - The subconscious mind is in a **deeply meditative state** as you wake up and as you fall asleep, this makes your **brain more receptive to suggestions.**
  - **Repeat an affirmation** as you wake up and right before you fall asleep.

Here are some good examples of **positive affirmations:**

- ***Everything is working out for me, no matter how it feels at any give point and time.***
- ***I am so incredibly lucky and happy to be alive.***
- ***I don't chase, I attract, everything I desire simply comes to me.***
- ***I am so excited for what's coming next.***
- ***Today is going to be an incredible day!***
- ***I have everything that I want and am excited for tomorrow.***

Write down your daily affirmation in your own words (copy to your notes app to remember):

____

____

____

____

Write down your morning affirmation in your own words:

____

____

____

____

Write down your night affirmation in your own words:

____

____

____

____

3. Positive Self Talk

Okay so you're starting to understand how your words and thoughts are **creating your reality.**

Now what about all that **negative things** you say about yourself and about life in general? How do you **talk to yourself?**

Is there something that you **say out loud or in your head** that's negative. Some examples;

- "I feel ugly"
- "I'm so dumb"
- "I'm so over it"
- "I'm never going to find someone"
- "I have terrible luck"
- "Everything is so hard"
- "I'm so miserable all the time"
- "Why is life so shit?"

Remember, your brain is **believing** all of these words and it will **focus on bringing you evidence to prove that the words are true.**

So, what are **3 negative things that you repeatedly say?** Write them down.

____

____

____

____

What are you going to **replace these words** with when you next catch yourself saying it?

____

____

____

____

4. Mirror Work Mantra

This one's pretty simple but something **you've probably never done.**

Every time you catch yourself in the mirror look into your eyes and say a positive mantra to yourself; **something like "damn I'm f***ing sexy" or "I feel incredible today" or "I'm crushing it today".**

Use words that **resonate with you** but make sure they are **positive**.

Remember to **attach a feeling** to the words.

Even on days you don't believe it, **make it a habit.**

Be as **outrageous** with your mirror work mantras as you'd like - switch it up, keep it light, have fun with it.

Make it short - **make an impact with it.**

Write down your mirror work mantra:

____

____

____

____

Say it out loud when you're alone and **in your head** when people are around (we don't want them to think you're crazy).

Try to practice this mirror work mantra as often as possible, it'll start to **become a habit** and you'll find yourself **automatically saying it when you look in the mirror.**

You might even **start to really believe it.**

5. You vs Your Phone

When you wake up in the morning, **what's the first thing that you do?**

Grab your phone? Thought so.

When you wake up, your brain is transitioning from a **theta state—a deeply relaxed, borderline meditative state—to a more alert alpha or beta state.**

This is a crucial time for **setting intentions and framing your mindset for the day.** Reaching for your phone **disrupts this process.**

You wouldn't let **100 people walk into your bedroom** first thing in the morning would you? When you grab your phone, **you basically do.**

It sends your brain **into a reactive mode**, absorbing external stimuli like **texts, socials, and emails.**

This can cause a **spike in stress hormones** and conditions your brain to be **more reactive and less intentional throughout the day.**

In essence, you're forfeiting your first moments of the day to external circumstances, instead of **consciously steering them to align with your own well-being and goals.**

We know that this one is going to be hard **but you're here to make changes**, right?

And you're probably going to fail some days, **but that's okay, try again the next day.**

Here's what to do on **days that you do remember:**

- Realize that you're waking up - oh hey.
- Consciously stop yourself from touching your phone.
- Stay in your bed and lay on your back
- Take 10 deep breaths, **inhaling through the mouth** and **exhaling through the mouth**
- **Repeat your morning affirmation as you breathe.**
- Take a moment to lay in a calm state after your breaths

Then when you're done - grab your phone - **we know you want to.**

This is a really interesting **you vs you moment. Your mind and body will fight you on this.**

The question is - **who will win?**

6. Breathwork

If you ever find yourself in a **mental spiral** or feeling **particularly stressed**, you can use **breathwork to regulate your nervous system and redirect your thoughts**.

Why breathwork?

Ever notice your **breath shorten** when you're **stressed** or a**nxious?**

It shortens so much sometimes that it **sends the body into shock** and leads to a **panic attack.**

When your breath is shortened, it **signals to the brain** that there's **something to fear**, like there's a **predator around the corner.**

Every emotion is **connected to your breath,** so if you can **control your breath**, you can **control your emotions.**

When you take **slow, deep breaths**, you're sending **signals to your brain to relax.**

Deep breathing activates the **vagus nerve**, the largest nerve in the body, that connects the brainstem to all of your major organs and **is responsible for <u>regulating emotion.</u>**

Stimulating this nerve **kicks your parasympathetic nervous system** into gear—that's the "**rest and digest**" part of your autonomic nervous system.

This **counters the stress-induced "fight or flight"** mode, **dialing down the production of stress hormones like cortisol.**

What you get is a **calmer mind, lower heart rate**, and a **sense of equilibrium**, making it **easier to tackle any thoughts or challenges that come your way.**

So, the next time you breathe deeply, know that you're doing some **instant neuroscience to get your system back on track.**

Tips for Breathwork

1. Focus your mind on the breath.
2. When you catch yourself thinking, redirect your mind to the breath.
3. Make your breath slow and deep - the deeper you inhale the more intense the experience.
4. You can choose to play ambient music or binaural beats during technique 1 & 2
5. Increase the timer of each breathwork practice as you get more comfortable.

Please Note:

- These techniques can be quite intense; you will feel sensations in the body and may feel a strong emotional release - if so, let it out.
- Your body will try to fight you on continuing the breath, but that's okay, continue until the timer sounds.
- If you feel uncomfortable at any point, please stop the practice.

Breathwork Technique 1

Quick Focused Breath:

1. Set a timer for 2 minutes, ensure that the alarm is soft and low volume
2. Sit or lie down in a quiet, comfortable, safe space with your spine straight
3. Close your eyes.
4. Take 3 normal breaths in and out to settle in.

Let's begin:

1. Take one deep inhale through your nose, let your belly inflate like a balloon, then;
2. Take one short inhale through the nose, up to your chest, then;
3. Hold at the top of your head for 6-8 seconds, followed by;
4. One long exhale for 6-8 seconds through the mouth like you're blowing out a candle
5. Repeat the breath till the timer sounds

Stay in this state of calm for as long as you'd like

- Allow any thoughts or feelings to arise and simply watch your thoughts
- Once you're ready slowly open your eyes

Breathwork Technique 2

Mouth Breathing Technique:

- Set a timer for 3-5 minutes, ensure that the alarm is soft and low volume
- Lie down flat on the floor or bed with no pillow, ensure that your spine is straight
- Place one hand on your lower belly and the other on your chest
- Close your eyes
- Take 3 normal breaths in and out to settle in.

Let's begin:

- Inhale through the mouth and into the belly
- Without exhaling inhale again through the mouth up into the chest
- Let your exhale simply fall out of your mouth with an audible sigh
- Repeat this pattern with no breaks.

After your alarm sounds, lay in this feeling for an extended period of time

- Allow any thoughts or feelings to arise and simply watch your thoughts
- Once you're ready slowly open your eyes

Breathwork Technique 3

When you're feeling overwhelmed in public try this shortened technique:

Take a second to clear your mind

1. Inhale deeply through the nose into your belly
2. Inhale again up to your chest
3. Hold it at the top of your head for 3 seconds
4. Let go through the mouth like you're blowing out a candle
5. Repeat 3 times or until feeling calm

CHAPTER 4

RECOGNIZING THE FREEZE STATE

"In the realm of trauma, the freeze state is a sanctuary of numbness, where feelings and reality are held at bay."

- Bessel A. Van Der Kolk

Understanding the Freeze State

Hopefully at this point you've learnt some **really cool stuff about how your brain works.**

Now let's dive into how **avoidant attachment** often fall into a **"freeze state"** pattern in relationships.

The freeze response or the dorsal vagal state is your **nervous system's safety mechanism.**

When the system is **overwhelmed** by **stress** or **perceived threats** to your **emotional safety**, the dorsal vagal response acts to **dampen your emotional engagement**, leading to a state of **detachment or numbness.**

This response, deeply rooted in the primal need for **self-preservation**, manifests as an **avoidance of vulnerability and intimacy.**

It's a **coping mechanism,** a way to **emotionally shut down** and **protect yourself** from the **potential pain of emotional exposure.**

The freeze response can be seen as an **internal retreat**, a way to **maintain control** and **distance** in relationships, effectively **minimizing the risk of rejection.**

This state of **disconnection**, however, <u>**comes at a cost**</u>, **limiting the depth and quality of personal connections.**

What are your go to moves to emotionally shut down or distance yourself in relationships?

____

____

____

____

____

____

Recognizing Controlling Patterns

In avoidant attachment style, the **urge to control** often stems from a deep-seated **fear of loss or rejection.**

Unpredictability or too much pressure in relationships, leads to behaviors that attempt to **set harsh boundaries** and **take control**.

This need for control is a **protective strategy**, but often **makes things worse.**

Control behaviors are usually a response to **underlying anxiety.**

For example, you might set a boundary by **limiting physical closeness or affection** with your partner because you subconsciously **fear emotional closeness.**

This controlled behavior **creates distance** and makes it easier for you to **emotionally disconnect and shut down.**

Who is someone you have emotionally shut down with? What control behaviors did you use to shut down?

____

____

____

____

What do you think was the trigger that made you emotionally distance yourself in this relationship?

____

____

____

____

IS IT A BOUNDARY OR IS IT A FREEZE RESPONSE?

Ask yourself

1. Is Your Boundary Reasonable?

Wanting some space in a relationship is healthy and reasonable.

2. Are You Feeling Vulnerable?

Are you experiencing a level of closeness that is making you feel too vulnerable? What is the reason you need space?

3. Is Your Boundary Actually a Freeze Response?

Using space as a way to avoid intimacy and create distance is a freeze response and avoidant pattern.

4. Do You Need to Communicate Your Needs?

Don't pull back or isolate, if you require more space, communicate this need clearly.

5. Do You Need to Adjust Your Boundary?

If it is rooted in avoidance, this boundary should be adjusted.

If it is a reasonable boundary that isn't being respected then you should consider what's best for you.

What is a reasonable boundary you had in a past relationship that wasn't respected?

Did you communicate your needs? If so, what did you say; if not, what should you have said?

How did you respond when the need was not being met?

What are some boundaries rooted in avoidance that you should let go of?

CHAPTER 5

YOUR SHADOW WORK JOURNAL

"Until you make the unconscious conscious it will direct your life and you will call it fate."

- Carl Jung

YOUR SHADOW WORK JOURNAL

What is the Shadow Self?

We all have a "shadow self"; this is the part of the subconscious mind where we store all of our **deepest shame, regret, denial and desires**.

It's the part of us that we hide from the world. In the context of **avoidant attachment** style, the shadow may include fears of **intimacy, vulnerability, and dependency.**

It can manifest as **emotional detachment, a deep-seated need for independence,** and a **resistance to forming deep emotional connections.**

The more we repress these parts of ourselves **the darker our shadow self becomes**.

These emotional blockages lead to **self sabotaging behaviour, anxiety and negativity.**

Shadow work helps to **access these parts of yourself** to experience a release of these **repressed feelings.**

What is Shadow Work?

Shadow work is a simple but powerful practice where you **answer questions** relating to your childhood and adult life to **determine your patterns of behaviour.**

It was first derived by renowned psychoanalyst Carl Jung who believed that our shadow self is **predominantly developed during childhood**.

Prompts about **childhood are integral to the practice** to understand where your behaviour manifests from.

These prompts will help to access parts of the subconscious brain that store your **deepest memories, beliefs** and **assumptions about the world**.

These are the traits that are deeply programmed in the mind that you **barely even recognize in yourself**.

As you answer the prompts you will **unearth answers** that **you might not have even been aware of.**

The Role of Trauma

Now that you're aware of what shadow work is, you've probably realized that you'll be **confronting some past trauma** with your shadow work prompts.

It's important here to understand the context of **the word "trauma"** as we're using it.

Big "T" Trauma

"Big T" traumas include events that are generally recognized as traumatic by society.

They're usually **significant, shocking, or catastrophic** occurrences such as emotional or sexual abuse, violence, or other life-threatening situations.

Small "t" Trauma

"Small t" traumas might not be life-threatening or as immediately shocking, but they still carry a **significant emotional weight**.

They include things like when a child is **emotionally neglected, dismissed, confused about their identity, overly disciplined, limited in expression, ignored, controlled, smothered, passively bullied or had too many expectations placed on them.**

Maybe your parent/s were just **too busy trying to support the family,** maybe they were **trying their best** but also **struggling with their own issues.**

The terms "big T" and "small t" **do not imply** that one type of trauma is more important or impactful than the other.

The impact of trauma is subjective and **varies greatly from person to person**. Both types can lead to **lasting emotional pain that affect you into adulthood.**

Understanding these **root causes is crucial for healing**.

It allows you to recognize that your **coping mechanisms served a purpose** at one point, even if they're **no longer serving you now.**

It's **not about assigning blame,** but about **understanding and compassion.**

Your Shadow Work Journal

Now that we've delved into the concept of shadow work, it's time to **put theory into practice**.

This section is designed to help you **explore your 'shadow' through a series of prompts.**

Each set of prompts focuses on a different aspect of your relationship and personal history. We'll deep dive the following:

1. Childhood Reflection
2. Assessing Current Patterns
3. Embracing Vulnerability
4. Dating, Sex & Relationships
5. Focusing on Personal Growth
6. Envisioning the Future

Remember, shadow work is a **personal and often emotional process.**

It's okay to feel **uncomfortable** at times.

That discomfort is a sign that **you're pushing your boundaries and growing.**

Tips For Shadow Work Journalling

- **Create a safe space:** Find a quiet and comfortable space where you can focus on your thoughts and emotions without distractions. Set up your space so that you feel calm and safe.

- **Write Freely:** This journal is a judgement-free zone. Let your thoughts flow freely on the pages. Don't worry about sounding 'correct' or 'proper'. Just write what feels right for you, in your own voice.

- **Choose prompts that resonate with you:** If they make you feel uncomfortable then they're usually the ones you should answer.

- **Focus on the Details**: Go into as much detail as you can when writing your answers

- **Don't hold back:** This journal is just for you, there should be no shame or fear when practicing. You don't have to share it with anyone unless you want to. It's a safe container for your thoughts, emotions, dreams, fears, and hopes.

- **No Wrong Answers:** In this journal, every answer is the right one because it's yours. Your experiences, your feelings, your perspectives – they all matter. Each prompt is an invitation for self-exploration, not a test.

- **Allow emotions to surface:** If you feel any intense emotions bubbling let them out!

- **Embrace Creativity:** Feel free to use different forms of creative expression. If words don't feel sufficient, you can draw, sketch, doodle, use colors, write poems, or even create a collage. This journal is your canvas.

- **Consistency and Flexibility:** You can practice over days, weeks or months. Aim for consistency, but don't stress if life gets hectic and you miss a day or two. The important thing is to come back when you can. If you want to spend more time on a particular exercise, alter the question or skip one that doesn't resonate, that's perfectly fine. This journey is about you and should be adapted to your rhythm.

- **Be kind to yourself:** if it feels overwhelming take a break.

CHAPTER 6

CHILDHOOD REFLECTION

"Much of what we call personality is not a fixed set of traits, only coping mechanisms a person acquired in childhood."

- Dr. Gabor Mate

CHILDHOOD REFLECTION

Shadow Work & Your Inner Child

Your shadow work journey starts with some **deep childhood reflection**. This is going to help you understand **where your patterns of behavior started.**

Your inner child is that part of your psyche that **still reacts and feels like the child you once were.**

It carries your **experiences, memories, and emotions** from your early years.

As we grow older, many of us **suppress** this part of ourselves to fit into societal norms and expectations, leading to **unaddressed emotional turmoil** that can have a significant impact on our lives.

Shadow work is the process of **acknowledging, understanding, and healing this hidden part of yourself.**

It involves **addressing the unmet needs, unrecognized desires, and unresolved emotions of your inner child.**

By engaging in this **profound self-reflection process**, you can identify the **origins of your fears, insecurities, and patterns of behavior** that may be holding you back.

Shadow work can help us understand these experiences, see how they **shaped our attachment styles,** and **allow us to heal** and move towards a healthier way of relating to others.

We'll help you **bring light to your shadow**, giving it the **attention, love, and understanding it needs to heal.**

Through this healing, you can start **reshaping your fears**, releasing your attachment to certain outcomes, and **begin embracing self love.**

Ready to get started?

CHILDHOOD REFLECTION

What did you think about your parent/s' relationship growing up?
Write about them from your childhood perspective.

How do you view their relationship as an adult?

CHILDHOOD REFLECTION

As a child who was the first person to ever let you down? Do you remember that moment? What happened?

How did you feel about them after it happened?

How did it change the way you thought and acted toward others?

CHILDHOOD REFLECTION

Were you allowed to express your emotions as a child? What was the reaction to you expressing yourself?

Write about a time that you expressed your emotions and were rejected as a child.

CHILDHOOD REFLECTION

How did your parent/s talk about success at home? What was their mentality toward money, discipline and working?

Have any of their thoughts rubbed off on you? If so, what and is it a healthy mindset?

CHILDHOOD REFLECTION

When you achieved anything as a child did your parent/s encourage and validate your achievement? Did you feel supported or did you feel pressured?

How do you view achievements as an adult? Do you put a lot of pressure on yourself? How does perceived failure affect you?

CHILDHOOD REFLECTION

Reflect on what was your most traumatic experience as a child.
What happened?

How did this make you feel about yourself? Did it change you?

How do you think this affects you as an adult? Can you identify any fears that stem from this experience?

CHILDHOOD REFLECTION

What was one strong belief that you had as a child that you were wrong about?

What changed your mind?

Have you fully released this belief or do you think it still lingers? Why?

CHILDHOOD REFLECTION

Were there ever times when you felt like you had to hide or change parts of yourself from your family? What were they?

Are you still hiding parts of yourself? If so, what and why?

What would you say to your childhood self about these parts of you?

CHILDHOOD REFLECTION

How were conflicts handled in your childhood home? Did your parent/s fight, bicker or argue in front of you? Explain the dynamic.

How has this influenced your conflict resolution in relationships as an adult?

CHILDHOOD REFLECTION

Did you ever feel burdened as a child, like you took on too much responsibility, whether literally or emotionally? Explain.

How do you think this changed you?

What would you say to your childhood self about this responsibility?

CHILDHOOD REFLECTION

When you think about your bond with you mother/mother figure, what stands out? How did you feel about her as a child?

Can you see any of her traits in you now? What are they? Are they good, bad or both? How do you feel about her as an adult?

CHILDHOOD REFLECTION

When you think about your bond with your father/father figure, what stands out? How did you feel about him as a child?

Can you see any of his traits in you now? What are they?
Are they good, bad or both? How do you feel about him as an adult?

CHILDHOOD REFLECTION

Did you have an anxious, very stoic or strict parent? If so, how do you think their moods affected you as a child?

Did you pick up any of these patterns of behavior as a child? If so, what?

Can you recognize any of these patterns in you now? If so, how does it affect you?

CHILDHOOD REFLECTION

Were there instances in your childhood where you were punished or shamed for showing vulnerability? What happened?

How do you think this affects your adult relationships?

When was the last time you struggled with vulnerability?

CHILDHOOD REFLECTION

How did you seek comfort as a child? Were you encouraged to self-soothe, or was comfort available from others around you?

What coping mechanisms did you build from this?

Do you feel comfortable reaching out for comfort as an adult? Why/why not?

CHILDHOOD REFLECTION

How did you feel your parent/s perceived you as a child? What was their belief about who you were and how did they speak about you?

How do you feel this impacted your self perception as a child?

Are you still this same version of yourself or have you changed? If so, how?

CHILDHOOD REFLECTION

Take some time to draw something that your childhood self used to draw and connect with that version of you.

CHILDHOOD REFLECTION

Were there instances growing up when you felt that your personal boundaries were ignored or not respected? What happened?

Does this still trigger you today? How do you react?

How do you communicate those boundaries, if at all?

CHILDHOOD REFLECTION

How did your parent/s speak to each other? How was affection, if at all, shown in your childhood home?

How do you speak to partners, do you show affection in the same way that your parent/s did? Is this healthy or does it need a change?

CHILDHOOD REFLECTION

Write a letter to your mother/mother figure about your childhood. What do you want them to know about how you felt?

CHILDHOOD REFLECTION

Write a letter to your father/father figure about your childhood. What do you want them to know about how you felt as a child?

CHILDHOOD REFLECTION

Imagine meeting your 8 year old self. What advice would you give them for the coming years? Start with *dear your name*.

CHILDHOOD REFLECTION

If your childhood self could see you now, what would they think? Would they be surprised at who you have become? Why?

What would your childhood self want for you? Write in their tone of voice.

CHILDHOOD REFLECTION

What avoidant attachment style patterns in your relationships can you identify that you developed during childhood?

What do you think you need to work on moving forward?

CHAPTER 7

ASSESSING CURRENT PATTERNS

"What you resist, persists."

- Carl Jung

ASSESSING CURRENT PATTERNS

What does your inner narrative sound like? How do you talk to yourself when you're alone?

What's a recurrent avoidant thought that you have, something that pops up randomly? Explain it.

Why do you think that this comes up so often? What is your mind trying to protect you from?

ASSESSING CURRENT PATTERNS

What is your view on love in general?
Do you believe in it? Do you think you will ever find true love?

Can you think of someone's relationship that you wish you could emulate? What about them do you admire?

ASSESSING CURRENT PATTERNS

Can you think of a time when you felt someone was becoming too dependent on you? Who was it? What did they do?

How did you react?

Was this a valid reaction?

ASSESSING CURRENT PATTERNS

Do you unintentionally dismiss or invalidate the emotions and needs of others? Do you avoid deep conversations? Write about a specific time you did this.

Why do you think you do this? How do you feel when someone is expressing their emotions to you?

ASSESSING CURRENT PATTERNS

Do you ever ask for help? If so, how does it feel?
If not, why not?

Do you think asking for help is weak? How do you feel about someone when they ask you for help?

When was a time that you should have reached out for help but didnt?

ASSESSING CURRENT PATTERNS

Are there any deep seated beliefs or assumptions that you have about love? What are they?

Can you pinpoint where these beliefs started?

Do you think these beliefs are healthy? If so why, if not what needs to change?

ASSESSING CURRENT PATTERNS

Describe a time that you sabotaged an opportunity to create a deep connection with someone. Who was it with and what happened? Tell the story.

Why did you do it?

Do you regret it? What would you do differently now?

ASSESSING CURRENT PATTERNS

Do you struggle to trust? Why? What do you fear will happen if you trust someone?

How can you lower these walls for someone that deserves your trust? Is there anyone that you can think of that deserves more openness from you? Who is it and why would you want to open up?

ASSESSING CURRENT PATTERNS

Draw lines out from "My Circle" of every person in your life that you trust right now.

ASSESSING CURRENT PATTERNS

Why do you trust each of these people? Do you open up to them? Who didn't make the cut and why?

ASSESSING CURRENT PATTERNS

Describe the ways you may intellectualize or create excuses to avoid engaging with your emotions. Do you tend to talk yourself out of liking someone? How do you do it? Write out what goes through your mind.

ASSESSING CURRENT PATTERNS

What do you love about your independence?
Write about it in detail.

What do you feel like you might lose if you commit to someone? Why?

ASSESSING CURRENT PATTERNS

What's your most toxic trait?
Explain in detail.

How would you judge someone else who does the same thing? Be honest.

ASSESSING CURRENT PATTERNS

Who's someone you really liked but purposely pushed away? Tell the story of what was going through your head to justify pushing them away.

ASSESSING CURRENT PATTERNS

When you feel stressed, do you tend to isolate or engage with distractions? What do you do to isolate and what forms do these distractions usually take?

What is your most toxic distraction and why do you turn to it?

ASSESSING CURRENT PATTERNS

Have you ever avoided making plans for the future? What happens inside of your head when you think too far forward?

Is it because you know that you don't like the person enough to commit or is it because you fear commitment itself?

ASSESSING CURRENT PATTERNS

Do you find it hard to express your feelings? What happens when you're put on the spot?

What do you fear could happen if you express yourself openly?

ASSESSING CURRENT PATTERNS

Have you ever felt uncomfortable receiving affection or praise? If so, why do you think you react this way?

What does receiving affection and praise mean to you?

What do you think would happen if you embraced it?

ASSESSING CURRENT PATTERNS

Do you tend to keep your personal life and feelings private, even from those close to you? Why do you think this is?

Who is someone that you have comfortably opened up to? Why did you choose them?

How does opening up to this person make you feel?

ASSESSING CURRENT PATTERNS

How much of your identity is tied to your independence? Explain how this has shaped your relationships and self-perception.

Will it be hard to let this part of you go? How can you be more open to letting someone in?

ASSESSING CURRENT PATTERNS

Do you use sarcasm or humor as a defense mechanism to avoid vulnerability? How do you do it and does it work?

Has anyone ever called you out on this? If so, what did they say?

Why do you think you do it?

ASSESSING CURRENT PATTERNS

Do you feel comfortable having deep conversations about yourself? When it's time to talk about you do you open up? Why?

What are you afraid that people will see or believe about you?

CHAPTER 8

EMBRACING VULNERABILITY

"Staying vulnerable is a risk we have to take if we want to experience connection."

- Brené Brown

EMBRACING VULNERABILITY

Did you ever see your father/father figure embrace vulnerability growing up? How did he perceive it? How did he hold himself?

Do you think you picked up some of his habits? If so which ones? Are they healthy? Why/why not?

EMBRACING VULNERABILITY

Can you remember a time that your father/father figure taught you about what it means to be a man/woman? What did he say?

How do you think he influenced the way you love? Is it healthy? Why/why not?

EMBRACING VULNERABILITY

Did you ever see your mother/mother figure embrace vulnerability? How did she perceive it? How did she hold herself?

Do you think you picked up some of her habits? If so which ones? Are they healthy? Why/why not?

EMBRACING VULNERABILITY

Can you remember a time that your mother/mother figure taught you about what it means to be a man/woman? What did she say?

How do you think she has influenced the way you love? Is it healthy? Why/why not?

EMBRACING VULNERABILITY

What does vulnerability mean to you? Is it a strength or a weakness? Why do you see it that way?

Have you been hurt in a moment of vulnerability? What happened?

Have you felt supported or understood in a moment of vulnerability? What happened?

EMBRACING VULNERABILITY

What's something you wish you said to someone that you haven't yet?
Write it out.

Who are they to you and why haven't you said it?

EMBRACING VULNERABILITY

When was the last time you cried? What happened? Explain in detail.

Did it feel cathartic or did you feel shame afterward? Why?

EMBRACING VULNERABILITY

Is there anyone in your life that still treats you like a 'version of you' that no longer exists? Who is it and how does it make you feel?

How can you express to them that you've changed?

How can you let go if they can't change their perception of you?

EMBRACING VULNERABILITY

Think of a time when your vulnerabilities were exposed without your consent. What happened?

How did you react, how did that make you feel?

EMBRACING VULNERABILITY

Do you believe you need to be strong all the time? What does strength mean to you?

When was a time that being strong made you feel good?

When was a time that being strong felt isolating and lonely?

EMBRACING VULNERABILITY

What's something you've been too afraid to say out loud?

EMBRACING VULNERABILITY

Have you ever withheld your feelings to maintain an image of being 'unfazed' or 'tough'? Explain a relationship where you did this and how you did it.

How did you really feel?

EMBRACING VULNERABILITY

What's the most vulnerable thing you're willing to share about yourself right now? Don't hold back.

EMBRACING VULNERABILITY

What's a past trauma you really need to consciously get over?

How can you forgive yourself for holding onto this for too long?

EMBRACING VULNERABILITY

Imagine meeting your 16 year old self. What would you tell them about romantic relationships? What advice would you give? Start with *dear name*

CHAPTER 9

DATING, SEX & RELATIONSHIPS

"The primary cause of unhappiness is never the situation but your thoughts about it."

- Eckhart Tolle

DATING, SEX & RELATIONSHIPS

If you had the chance to revisit a past relationship and change one thing, what would it be?

Can you forgive yourself? What would you do differently next time?

DATING, SEX & RELATIONSHIPS

Do you think you've ever actually been in love? If so, with who and how did it feel? If not, why not?

What does being in love look like to you?

DATING, SEX & RELATIONSHIPS

When was the last time you pushed someone away because they were getting emotionally close? Who was it and why did you do it?

What was your internal narrative telling you during this time? Write it all out.

DATING, SEX & RELATIONSHIPS

Have you ever felt abandoned or heartbroken in a relationship? Who was the person & how did it end?

How did this affect your ability to trust and form new relationships?

DATING, SEX & RELATIONSHIPS

Have you ever avoided discussing your feelings with a partner? Who was it with and what were you avoiding?

How did this impact your relationship?

What would you do differently now?

DATING, SEX & RELATIONSHIPS

Do you have boundaries in your relationships that are non-negotiable? What are they?

Why are they important to you?

Do you think they're reasonable boundaries or avoidant tactics? Why?

DATING, SEX & RELATIONSHIPS

What is something you have done in a past relationship that you knew was wrong?

How did your partner respond? What was the result?

What would you do differently now?

DATING, SEX & RELATIONSHIPS

How do you handle disagreements in your relationships? Do you confront them or avoid them? Why?

When was a time you regretted your reaction?

What would you do differently now?

DATING, SEX & RELATIONSHIPS

How do you use dating apps? Are you looking for something serious or casual? Why?

Do you think your relationship to dating is healthy? Does the way you date fullfill you?

Who has been the most memorable connection from the apps? What happened with that person?

DATING, SEX & RELATIONSHIPS

Do you find it difficult to express your needs?
Why/why not?

What are your coping mechanisms when your needs aren't being met? Do you self isolate, if so, why?

When was the last time you expressed a need to someone? How did they respond?

DATING, SEX & RELATIONSHIPS

Thinking back to your greatest heartbreak, what could you have done differently in that relationship?

What's something you regret doing?

Were they good for you? Why/ why not?

DATING, SEX & RELATIONSHIPS

Do you think being in a committed relationship means you have to sacrifice your independence or freedom? Why?

Do you think you'll ever find someone who doesn't make you feel this way? Why/ why not? What parts of your independence are you willing to let go of to make room for someone else?

DATING, SEX & RELATIONSHIPS

What was the biggest relationship drama that you had? Did you self sabotage? Explain the story in detail from your perspective.

Now explain the story from their perspective.

Did your perspective change after writing two versions? What would you do differently in this situation?

DATING, SEX & RELATIONSHIPS

What sacrifices did you make in your most significant relationship?

Did you feel appreciated? Why/Why not?

How did this relationship shape the way you see your future relationships?

DATING, SEX & RELATIONSHIPS

Do you feel shameful about any of your past exes?
Why?

Write a short letter forgiving yourself for staying in this relationship and let any shameful feelings go.

DATING, SEX & RELATIONSHIPS

Is there an ex you still think about? If so, who are they and why do you still think about them?

Do you think you romanticize this person? Were they actually good for you? Why/why not?

What would you have done differently with them?

DATING, SEX & RELATIONSHIPS

Write down everything you loved and everything you hated about being with your ex. Don't be shy.

Loved

Hated

DATING, SEX & RELATIONSHIPS

Have you ever been cheated on in a relationship? If so, why do you think this happened? Do you blame yourself? Why?

How did it change you?

How can you trust again?

DATING, SEX & RELATIONSHIPS

Who is someone you had an intense sexual connection with? Was the emotional connection there too? How did the sex make you feel before and after? How did this relationship play out?

DATING, SEX & RELATIONSHIPS

Do you enjoy casual relationships? How does casual sex serve you? Explain what it does for you.

How does sex with an emotional connection differ?

What do you want and need to have a fulfilling sex life?

DATING, SEX & RELATIONSHIPS

Do you have feelings for someone right now? Who is it? What do you love about them?

How does it feel to be around them, to talk to them?

Have you told them? What fears do you have about the relationship?

DATING, SEX & RELATIONSHIPS

After sex do emotional displays like cuddling, kissing and affection make you feel uncomfortable? Why/why not?

Does it depend on who you're with? When was a time this felt natural and comforting? If never, what would you like to become more comfortable with to help encourage connection?

DATING, SEX & RELATIONSHIPS

Does the thought of committing to a long-term relationship scare you? If so, why?

Do you think you'll ever meet someone who balances you out and doesn't take away from your independence? What qualities should you be looking for in a partner?

DATING, SEX & RELATIONSHIPS

Can you identify any repeated patterns in your past relationships? What are they? Give specific examples.

DATING, SEX & RELATIONSHIPS

How would you react if a partner asked you to open up more emotionally or to be more physically affectionate?

What do you think would happen if you actually tried it? How do you think it would feel to give yourself fully to someone new without holding back?

DATING, SEX & RELATIONSHIPS

Is there a someone in your life right now that you think of all of the time but purposely push away? Who are they? How do they make you feel? Honestly.

What are you afraid of in this situation?

DATING, SEX & RELATIONSHIPS

Describe moments of deep loneliness. What happens inside your head? How do you cope? Would you like to be in a relationship right now?

DATING, SEX & RELATIONSHIPS

Do you lie about yourself to dates/partners?
What is the lie you tell?

What fears do you have around being truly seen and known by them?

DATING, SEX & RELATIONSHIPS

Write a forgiveness letter to yourself for any past mistakes or regrets in relationships. Be as honest as you can.

DATING, SEX & RELATIONSHIPS

Write a goodbye letter to your ex. Let it all out. Let it go.

CHAPTER 10

FOCUSING ON PERSONAL GROWTH

"Personal growth is not a matter of learning new information but of unlearning old limits."

- Alan Cohen

FOCUSING ON PERSONAL GROWTH

Have you been practicing listening to your thoughts? What avoidant thought patterns have you started to notice?

How has noticing these thoughts changed how you view them?

What are some thoughts and feelings you still need to work on?

FOCUSING ON PERSONAL GROWTH

What have you learned about the role of vulnerability in personal growth? Write about a situation where allowing yourself to be vulnerable led to a positive outcome.

What are some ways you can still work on being more vulnerable with the right person? What parts of yourself do you need to share more of?

FOCUSING ON PERSONAL GROWTH

Every time you try something outside of your comfort zone you'll transform and grow. What's something that scares you that you'd really like to try?

What has held you back from trying it?

What are some steps you can take toward trying it?

FOCUSING ON PERSONAL GROWTH

Honestly write down areas where you could improve or change for your own well-being, not just for a relationship.

FOCUSING ON PERSONAL GROWTH

If you could change one thing about your self-perception, what would it be and why?

How can you start working toward this change?

FOCUSING ON PERSONAL GROWTH

What have you learned about your triggers and coping mechanisms?
What will you be working on?

What's a small victory you've had recently with something that triggered you?

FOCUSING ON PERSONAL GROWTH

Consider your social life. How can you improve or expand your connections and social support? Even if it's out of your comfort zone.

Can you reach out to anyone? If so, who and why? If not, how can you meet new people?

FOCUSING ON PERSONAL GROWTH

What is a conversation you've been avoiding? Write it out.

FOCUSING ON PERSONAL GROWTH

Reflect on your support system. Who can you really rely on? Write about them and why they're important to you.

How can you strengthen this relationships and others? How can you become comfortable leaning on others when you need support?

FOCUSING ON PERSONAL GROWTH

What have you learned about yourself, your past relationships, and what you want in a partner?

FOCUSING ON PERSONAL GROWTH

If you only had 6 months left to live what would you be doing?

What would you do less of?

Who would you spend more time with?

FOCUSING ON PERSONAL GROWTH

Look back at the person you were when you started this journal and compare it with the person you are now. What have you learned?

In what ways have you grown and changed?
What are you most proud of?

CHAPTER 11

ENVISIONING THE FUTURE

"Your imagination is your preview of life's coming attractions."

- Albert Einstein

ENVISIONING THE FUTURE

CONGRATS ON MAKING IT THIS FAR!

You've done a whole lot of work, **probably cried a little** and figured some things out about yourself that **you didn't even realize.**

Now we start getting to the fun stuff.

Who do you **<u>want</u> to become?** What does your **glow up era look like?**

And why does **visualization matter?**

We've already **learnt some cool stuff about the subconscious mind** and now we'll take it a step further.

A significant part of the subconscious mind's power lies in the **Reticular Activating System** (RAS).

Your RAS is a **network of neurons** located in the brainstem that play a critical role in gatekeeping information to **send to your conscious mind.**

You don't realize it but your brain is taking in **a <u>ton</u> of information everyday.**

Your brain can't possibly **store all of this information.**

So, your RAS acts as a filter, deciding **what information should be given attention and what to overlook.**

When you **visualize a desired future,** your RAS **becomes attuned to opportunities, information, and experiences aligned with that future.**

Just like that weird feeling when you **learn a new word** and then all of a sudden you start hearing it everywhere, your RAS will **tune into what you have laid out for your future plans** and **show you messaging to encourage action.**

In order to get what you want, you have to first **know** what you want, **visualize** what you want and **believe** that it is coming.

The Importance of Visualization

Before you start envisioning your future in the next set of prompts, we want to give you some **pointers for visualization.**

REMEMBER THAT

1. Thoughts are the language of the brain

- Our brains respond to our **thoughts and beliefs**, whether they're about our current reality or an imagined future.
- **Your thoughts and beliefs become your reality.**

2. Feelings are the language of the body

- Our body responds to our **feelings**, which are often the product of our thoughts.
- If we can **feel the emotions** of our desired future **now**, our body can be 'tricked' into thinking that **future is already our reality,** resulting in more positive thoughts.
- This has the affect of telling your brain's RAS to **focus on positive outcomes.**

3. Thoughts + feelings create a state of being:

- When our thoughts **(brain) and feelings (body) align,** we enter a state of being.
- This state can **influence our actions, choices, and experiences, which ultimately shapes our reality.**

4. Mental rehearsal is key

- Just as athletes mentally rehearse their performances, **we can mentally rehearse our desired future.**
- This process, done regularly, can **build neural pathways** in our brain that supports that future.

How to Visualize

Here's how to apply these teachings through visualization while doing shadow work:

1. Create a Clear Mental Picture

- Define **what your future looks like** in detail.
  - What do you look like?
  - What are you wearing?
  - What are you doing?
  - Who are you with?
  - What is your job?
  - Where do you live?

2. Feel the Future Now

- **Engage your emotions as you visualize.**
- Feel the joy, excitement, love, or peace of your future **now**.
- This convinces your body that this future is happening now and will help to reprogram the mind.

3. Mental Rehearsal

- Regularly visualize your future, **immersing yourself in the feelings it brings**.
- This practice, done over time, **reinforces the neural pathways** that align with this future.
- Now your mind will **look for evidence** of the truth of this version of your life.

4. Let Go

- **Detach from the outcome and trust the process.**
- Don't stress about how or when your desired future will manifest.
- Your job is to **create it mentally and emotionally, and then let it unfold naturally.**

5. Take Aligned Action

- **Visualization isn't a replacement for action;** it's a **catalyst**.
- Inspired ideas or opportunities will come to you – **act on them.**
- They're part of the path to your **visualized future.**

ENVISIONING THE FUTURE

Do you feel differently about your self concept after everything you've learned? Write about your new beliefs about yourself (remember that what you believe about yourself becomes your reality).

My Self Concept

ENVISIONING THE FUTURE

Envision the ultimate version of your life. What have you let go of? What have you gained?

Let go of

Gained

ENVISIONING THE FUTURE

Picture yourself being open and vulnerable in a relationship. How does it feel? What have you done to become more comfortable with vulnerability? What is your emotional relationship with your partner like?

ENVISIONING THE FUTURE

What is your biggest personal challenge right now? Explain in detail.

Imagine you've overcome it. How did you do it? Write out the steps.

ENVISIONING THE FUTURE

Close your eyes and imagine a future where you feel secure within yourself and have everything you desire. Sit in this feeling for a moment. What do you love about yourself, what do you look like, how do you feel, move, act?

ENVISIONING THE FUTURE

Visualize yourself accomplishing a major life goal. Focus on the feelings of success and accomplishment. What is the goal?

What are the steps you took to achieve this?

What impact has achieving this goal made on your self worth and confidence?

ENVISIONING THE FUTURE

What does financial freedom look like to you? What amount of money would you like to be making each year? How are you living with this amount of income? Explain in vivid detail.

How did you achieve this financial freedom? What does your daily life and work look like?

ENVISIONING THE FUTURE

Envision your future house/s in vivid detail. Where is it, what does it look like, how is it decorated, how does it feel to live here?

ENVISIONING THE FUTURE

Envision your future car/s, what are you driving? How does it feel to have your dream car? Where are you going in it?

ENVISIONING THE FUTURE

Close your eyes and picture yourself in a place that brings you joy. Sit in it for a minute, feel it all over your body. Where are you? What does it feel like? Who's there? What are you doing?

ENVISIONING THE FUTURE

Visualize where you want to travel, both solo and with a future partner. Where are you going and what are you doing there?

ENVISIONING THE FUTURE

Draw lines from the circle about everything you desire in a dream partner.

Perfect Person

ENVISIONING THE FUTURE

Imagine your perfect person. Write a list of physical and emotional qualities this person has.

Physical

Emotional

ENVISIONING THE FUTURE

How does this future partner:

Support you

Love you

ENVISIONING THE FUTURE

Write about your biggest passions and interests.

Does your partner/future partner need to share these interests. If so, which ones?

ENVISIONING THE FUTURE

What's their personality like? How do you hang out? What does it look like at home together?

ENVISIONING THE FUTURE

Draw everything you desire on this page.
It can be words, symbols, images.

ENVISIONING THE FUTURE

Picture yourself pursuing a passion or dream you've held back on, what is it? What's different in this reality? Explain in detail.

ENVISIONING THE FUTURE

Visualize your future self's daily routine. What habits have you incorporated for a healthier life? How does it feel to live this life?

ENVISIONING THE FUTURE

Picture a typical Friday night 1 year from now. What are you doing? Who are you with? What's making you smile?

ENVISIONING THE FUTURE

Picture your life one year from now, after consistently working on your personal growth. What changes do you see?

ENVISIONING THE FUTURE

Picture a day in your life 5 years from now. What does it look like from the moment you wake up to when you go to bed? Write a day in the life.

ENVISIONING THE FUTURE

Write down today's date and 10 goals that you want to accomplish in the next 12 months in the present tense. i.e. I earn... I feel... I achieve... I own... I am... I accomplish... I have...

ENVISIONING THE FUTURE

Look back at your list of 10 goals. If you had a magic wand and could have any one of these goals in the next 24 hours which one goal would have the greatest positive impact on your life? Answer the following:

My goal

My deadline for this goal

What do I have to do to accomplish this goal?

ENVISIONING THE FUTURE

Organize what you have to do into a goal check list:

- [ ]
- [ ]
- [ ]
- [ ]
- [ ]
- [ ]
- [ ]
- [ ]
- [ ]
- [ ]

Take action and do something everyday to work toward this goal.

ENVISIONING THE FUTURE

Based on your visions write a letter to yourself in the present tense about all of your hopes and dreams for your future self coming true. Start with "Dear *name*.

ENVISIONING THE FUTURE

ENVISIONING THE FUTURE

CHAPTER 12

ENTERING A NEW ERA

"And suddenly you know: it's time to start something new and trust the magic of beginnings."

- Johannes Eckhart

ENTERING A NEW ERA

Ummm, hi... it's **pretty crazy** that you made it this far!

Completing this journal is a testament to **how much** you want to become the **best version of yourself.**

You're not **just** thinking about it or talking about it, you're **doing the work** and you should be **so proud of that.**

As you continue on **remember that healing isn't linear.**

You're going to feel those **avoidant** feelings pop up again and again and **that's okay.** You're more **aware** of it now, so you'll be able to **self regulate** a lot easier.

Here are some things to do to **keep you on the right path to** experience **security in relationships.**

Daily Reflection

- Set an alarm on your phone at the end of the day for a daily reflection
- Spend a few moments writing about your day
- Explain how you're feeling in detail

Physically writing down all of your feelings on paper will not only make you more **conscious of your patterns,** it will also help you to **release any anxiety** that is being stored in the mind and body.

Keep a Dating Diary

If you're dating, **keep a diary** about it. This will help you to be **honest with yourself** about what's going.

Not only does this help you **process emotions**, it's also so **fun** to read about yourself from your own perspective.

You'll be surprised at **how much your feelings change** over short periods of time.

ENTERING A NEW ERA

Remember to Watch Your Thoughts

Remember to practice **watching your thoughts. Positive self talk** and **affirmations** will change everything.

Practice the Vulnerability

Allowing yourself to be **vulnerable** with trusted people is a significant step towards **overcoming fears of intimacy.**

Vulnerability can feel **daunting**, but it's essential for building trust and **deepening emotional connections.**

Start small and gradually share more of your inner thoughts and feelings as you **grow more comfortable.**

Independence and Interdependence

While valuing your **independence**, also recognize the importance of **interdependence** in **healthy relationships.**

A balance between the two allows you to maintain your sense of self while also engaging in **meaningful connections** with others.

This balance is key to **fulfilling relationships** that respect both autonomy and mutual support.

Visualize Your Desired Future

Continue to **visualize** everything that you desire and believe that it is coming to you.

Your **subconscious mind** will continue to focus on opportunities that **bring your desires toward you.**

When opportunities come your way, **take action.**

ENTERING A NEW ERA

Welcome to your new era.

We hope that you've **learnt some cool things** about neuroscience, your brain and how it's **possible to change and grow.**

You've made it through a **pretty intense journey of introspection and transformation**, dealing with your avoidant attachment style.

You may have **come to a few realizations about yourself** and life; and we hope this has helped.

You've taken a **deep dive into your past, observed your present through a new lens, and envisioned an empowering future**.

By gaining insights into the patterns and behaviors associated with avoidant attachment, you have taken a **significant step towards healing and creating healthier relationships**.

As you move forward, **celebrate each milestone and progress you make** in building healthier and more secure attachments.

Don't ever forget - **you are capable**, **you are resilient, and you are deserving of love, connection,** and **joy in all its forms.**

Keep this journal close.

Revisit it often to **remind yourself of how far you've come** and the resilience you've displayed.

And as you move forward, **remember to be gentle with yourself.**

Healing is a **journey**, not a destination.

You got this.